What's So Special About Today?

Kelsey N. Clark • ILLUSTRATED BY Ashley Belote

Headline Kids
an imprint of Headline Books, Inc.
Terra Alta, WV

What's So Special About Today?

by Kelsey N. Clark

illustrated by Ashley Belote

To order additional copies of this book, or for book publishing information, or to contact the author:

Headline Kids
P. O. Box 52
Terra Alta, WV 26764

Email: mybook@headlinebooks.com
www.headlinebooks.com

Ashley Belote—Art Director
Lucas Kelly—Design/Layout

Published by Headline Books
Headline Kids is an imprint of Headline Books

ISBN-13: 9781946664822

Library of Congress Control Number: 2019948216

PRINTED IN THE UNITED STATES OF AMERICA

I dedicate this story to my adventure-loving and big-dreaming kids.
You both are my inspiration to live the best life I can. Thank you for all the
big and little moments you give me. I am so blessed to be your mom.
Love, Mom

The early morning greets me.
The sunshine fills my eyes.

"It's a new day!"
Mom says, "Our own
beautiful prize."

"What do you mean?"
I ask. "What's so special
about today?"

"It's another day
of life," she whispers,
as the wind chimes
loudly play.

Why is that special? I wonder.
She gives me a little wink, "You my dear
boy, are much luckier than you think."

6

"Mind your manners," she says,
as she drops me off at school.
"Listen well and follow along,
mind your teacher's rules."

$7 + 2 = 9$

$6 + 7 = 42$

$10 - 11 = 1$

Throughout the day my mind runs wild.
I talk more than I should.
I do my best to sit real still, but I want to get into the woods.

$11 + 2 = 22$

$5 + 5 = 25$

$1 - 2 = 15$

I get off the bus, climb in the truck.
Mom asks, "What was the special part of your day?"
"The playground I guess…"
I never know what to say.

My baby sister greets me, and we
open the gate hand in hand,
    We race right down the road, yelling
to Mom, "Catch us if you can!"

11

The porch swing sways; we wait
for the sound of Dad's truck.
The cows graze the grass, and I
search for the seven-point buck.

"Mom, what was special about your day?" I ask as we sit and swing on the porch.

"My time with you," she replies, "For our lives are quick and short."

I ponder that thought, and wonder again, what is that supposed to mean?

I think of Sunday school, Heaven is kind of scary to me.

"Today is another opportunity," she says, "to experience the joys of your heart, fill your mind with wonders, and finish what you start."

"This life that you have is a blessing."
I ask, "What does that word mean?"

"Well your clothes
cover you up and your
shoes fit just right.
Your belly is full and you
have a pillow at night."

"God gave you this body, he gave you these capable hands to do His purpose...

His work, for His people and His land."

"God wrote this story on your heart,
it's the story of your life.
    He asks you to be thankful and true,
to be patient, forgiving, and kind."

"Ask Him for these very things, for they can be hard to have on your own.

When someone
hurts your heart, let
God hold your hand
and help you grow."

"It's up to you to live this way, to give Him of yourself every day…"

"Daddy home!" Sis interrupts, as she stumbles, making her way.

"What is heaven like?" I ask.
She sweetly smiles and says,
"A special place full of love,
Now bow your head to pray."

"Mommy, I think I finally know
what's so special about today.
It's God's gift of love for us that
never goes away."